There were some things he did not like about living in a castle.
Some things he did not like at all but he did them.

John liked all the animals in the castle. He played
with the dogs and sometimes he was allowed to
hold the hawks. He knew he had to be very gentle
with the hawks. But best of all he liked the horses.

John played in the stables whenever he had time.
He liked to be near the horses but he had not
always liked them.

5

John remembered that when he first came to the castle he was scared of the horses.
He remembered the first time that he saw Star.
Star was a very big horse. John would never forget the trick that the stable boy played on him.

On that day Sir Brian was going riding. He told
John to go to the stable and to tell the stable boy
that he wanted his horse, his hawk and one of his
dogs.

"Bring my horse to the castle gate," said Sir Brian. John ran to the stable and told the boys to get one of the dogs ready and a hawk.

John told the boy who looked after the horses that
Sir Brian was going riding and wanted one of his
horses.

"Good," said the stable boy. "You get him out, he's in there." He pointed to one of the stalls. "Get him out of the stall for Sir Brian," he said.

John saw one of the biggest animals he had ever seen in all his life. The stable boy had told him to get this horse out of the stall. But could he do it?

"Get him out," the stable boy had said. "Get him out of the stable." John was scared. The animal was so big.

"Get hold of him," shouted the stable boy, "go on get hold of him but be gentle with him."

"How can I be gentle with such a big animal?" said John. The boy grinned and went out of the stable.

John was scared, very scared. He jumped when a black shape shot past him! It was a stable cat. "I'm not scared of a cat!" said John to himself. "Even a town boy isn't scared by a cat, not even a black cat!"

John did not know how to get hold of the horse.
He was new to all of this.
"But I came to be a knight," he said. "I must not be
scared of a horse! Go on horse, move!" John said
to the animal. The horse did not move.

The stable boy came in with the dog. He had a
hawk on his arm. John did not want the boy to see
that he was scared. He did not want Sir Brian to
think that he was just a scared town boy.

John wanted to get the big horse out of the stable so much. "Come on, please," he said to the horse. He began to push.

The horse did not move. John pushed as hard as he could. There was no way that the horse was going to move for him.

Sir Brian came in to the stable. He saw John in the stall pushing the big horse. He knew that it was not one of his riding horses but Star, his war-horse.

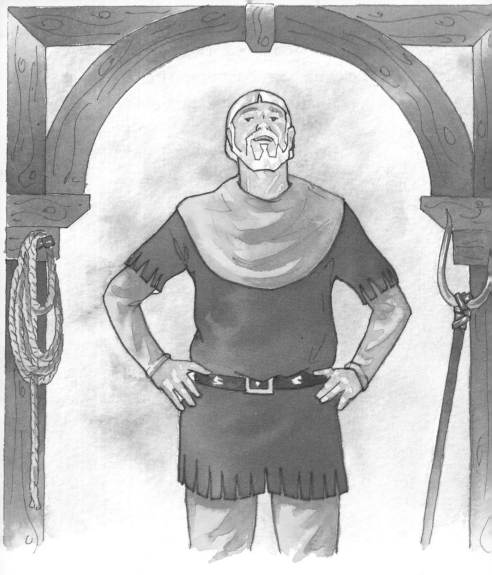

Sir Brian began to laugh. He guessed that the stable boy had played a trick on John because John was the new boy.

Then he remembered the first time he saw John when he was covered in grey flour. It was unkind to laugh at him.

"This is not one of my riding horses," he said, "this is Star. He is a war-horse, the biggest horse in the stables. Don't be scared of him, he might be a war-horse but he is very gentle."

Star began to move out of his stall.
"Not today, Star," said Sir Brian, "I'm not going to
war today, I'm just going riding."

John always remembered the first time he saw
Star. He was not scared of him now. John liked
Star best of all the horses he was so big and so
gentle.

John wanted to get hold of the stable boy. He had played a trick and made John scared. But never mind, Sir Brian had been kind, he had not laughed at him.